Contents

Look for the **Thinking Cap**.
When you see this picture, you will find
a problem to think about and write about.

The purple boots

A grand opening

Beep, beep! Elisa's father sounded the car horn. It was Elisa's birthday, and her dad was taking her out after school. She said a quick goodbye to her friends and ran to the car. She was excited. First they were going to the grand opening of her half-brother Juan's shoe shop. Then her dad was taking her out for a meal.

When they pulled up outside the shoe shop, they could see that it was filled with people and noisy chatter. Dad looked relieved. A reporter from the local newspaper was interviewing Juan. Elisa looked at all the shoes and listened to what people were saying. She heard great comments, such as 'wonderful design', 'high quality' and 'an amazing young talent'. Elisa felt proud of Juan.

After a while, the shop was quiet, and Juan came over. He had a present for Elisa. It was a pair of boots. 'I made them just for you,' he said. 'There are no others like them in the whole world, and they're purple – your favourite colour!'

School bus blues

On Monday morning, Elisa put on her new boots. They were very comfortable. When she looked in the mirror, she could see that they matched her purple jacket. It felt good to be wearing something other than her usual sneakers.

'Don't you look good!' said Mum, when Elisa went into the kitchen. 'Very nice, indeed,' agreed Dad.

On the school bus, some of the children noticed her new boots right away. 'What brand are they?' asked John.

John wore Core-brand trainers. At their school, most children whose parents could afford it wore either Core-brand or Purr-brand trainers. Other kids wore shoes that looked like Core or Purr trainers but cost a lot less. They bought them at places such as Super-Value Shoe Mart.

'What happened to your trainers?' asked Amy. 'Why did you wear those? I've never seen boots like *that* before.' Elisa looked down at her boots. She started to feel uncomfortable. She wished she were wearing her usual trainers. A wave of sadness washed over her. Juan had made those boots just for her. It was such a kind thing to do, and they did look good. So why didn't the other kids like them?

A best friend's opinion

When Elisa reached her classroom, her best friend Maya was already seated at her desk. Maya was about to begin a drawing for an art competition. Everyone knew Maya was the best artist in the school. She had already won several city art competitions and one regional competition. Maya looked up, and her eyes went straight to Elisa's new boots.

'Wow, what amazing boots!' she exclaimed. 'I love them. They're so different. They've got real personality.'

Immediately, Elisa started to cheer up. She valued Maya's opinion. Maya didn't always dress the same way as the other kids, but somehow she always looked great. Maya didn't care what others thought of her clothes, and people seemed to respect her for it.

Just then, Miss Diaz, their teacher, walked in. She also noticed Elisa's boots.

'What beautiful boots, Elisa,' she said. 'I'll bet they came from Juan's shop. You know, I went in there yesterday. His shoes have such style. I wish I could afford to buy them, but I'm afraid it's Super-Value Shoe Mart for me!'

The cheap shoe debate

A few weeks later, Juan came over for Sunday lunch. He handed Elisa's mum a packet of coffee. 'Hi, Cathy, this is for you and Dad,' he said.

'It's fair trade coffee from Uganda in Africa. I buy it because the workers there are paid a good wage for picking the coffee beans. In many other places, coffee-bean pickers are paid very little!'

Over lunch, Dad asked Juan how his business was going.

> Coffee beans grow in places such as Africa and South America, where many workers are poor. Fair trade coffee comes from coffee growers who take care of their staff.

'It's not good.' Juan told him. He looked glum. 'I get plenty of great comments, but not many sales.'

'My teacher likes your shoes,' Elisa told him, 'but she can't afford them. If you made them cheaper, I know she'd buy some.'

'That's the problem,' Juan said with a sigh. 'It costs a lot to make shoes in this country. The materials are expensive, and I have to pay the workers good wages. I can't compete with shoes made in countries where the workers are paid much less. Super-Value Shoe Mart **imports** crate-loads of shoes for very little.'

import to bring goods into a country from another country

10

'But don't we help the poor people in those countries if we buy their shoes?' asked Elisa.

'We'd help them much more if we paid enough money for them to be able to afford the same quality of life we have here,' Juan said. 'We have cheap shoes here only because other people work long hours for low wages elsewhere.'

'What about people here?' said Mum. 'It's good that most people can afford shoes these days. When Gran was young, most families had to save up for ages to buy shoes. Shoes were handed down from one child to another, and mended when they wore out.'

Another celebration

The next few months were tense. Everyone in the family was worried about Juan. He was still struggling to make his new business work. Every time they saw him, Juan seemed more stressed than the time before. Much of his time was spent travelling. He took samples of his shoes to department stores and large shoe-store chains to see if they would sell them. But the answer was always the same: *They're beautiful shoes, but we are looking for something less expensive.*

Write down your thoughts so that you can discuss these questions with a classmate.

1. Do you think your friends and classmates feel pressure to wear certain brands of clothes and shoes? Why or why not?

2. What do you think would happen to young designers if everyone bought only big-name brands?

3. Do you think it's fair that workers in some countries work long hours for little pay? Why do you think this happens?

4. What would happen here and overseas if we banned cheaper imported products altogether? Is there another solution?

Then one day, there was good news. A major department store had ordered some of Juan's shoes for its New York City branch. If the shoes sold well in New York, it would buy more shoes for its shops in other cities. Hopefully, this would turn out to be the big break Juan needed. That night, the family had a celebration dinner.

Everyone was proud of what Juan had accomplished through his hard work and determination.

What's the issue?

Hundreds of years ago, most goods that people used were made locally. Farmers sold their goods in nearby markets. Most villages had a blacksmith, who made metal goods. Women spun wool to make clothing. Only fancy items, such as silk and spices, came from far away. With the invention of the steam engine in the 1700s, large factories were able to produce vast quantities of goods. Suddenly, many goods, such as cotton fabrics, were being shipped to customers around the world.

Since then, transport has become faster and cheaper. More and more goods are being exported around the world. Richer countries, such as England, often buy goods from poorer countries, such as China. However, this can mean there are fewer manufacturing jobs in England. Also, the cheap prices paid for overseas goods mean some workers in the poorer countries continue to be poor.

In the Middle Ages, many goods were sold at local markets. At this French market, people bought items such as metalware and shoes.

Made to last

In the past, fewer cheap products were available. Most families owned fewer things. If they bought an item such as a lamp, it was probably well made but expensive. The owners would expect it to last for many years. If it broke, they would have it fixed, not buy a new one.

Look at this picture of a 1950s living room. This family had enough money to live well, but they had fewer possessions than many families have today.

These women work in a clothing factory in China. They make clothes for European and North American shops.

Did you know?

These days, people can often afford to throw out broken items and replace them. This was not the case in the past. We are now producing more rubbish than we used to, which is causing problems for the environment.

Big brands

Many big companies in countries such as the United States hire companies in poorer countries to make goods for them. Often the big companies sell these goods cheaply. For example, a shirt made in Vietnam might sell for only $20 in the United States. A small company that makes its clothes in the United States has to obey strict labour laws and health and safety laws. It cannot produce shirts as cheaply. Instead, it must rely on a reputation for high-quality products. If customers think that the company's shirts are better quality than the cheaper, imported shirts, people may buy them.

Big companies often sponsor famous people to use their brand of products. For example, they will give a sports star money and free clothing as long as he or she helps advertise the company's clothing or sports equipment. The company is happy because when fans see the player with the company's products, they are encouraged to buy this brand of clothing.

Small companies have another problem. Big companies spend lots of money on advertising. They try to convince people that their brand is the most fashionable. This allows them to sell cheaply made, imported clothing at high prices. Many people are willing to pay more money to be fashionable.

Put on your thinking cap

Write down your thoughts so that you can discuss these questions with a classmate.

1. Why do you think people buy brand-name products? Would you be most likely to buy an unknown brand of soft drink or a known brand? Why?

2. What clothing brands are fashionable with your friends? How can people who cannot afford these brands fit in?

3. Do you try to wear particular brands? If so, why do you choose these brands? Think about things such as advertising and peer pressure.

4. Would you be more likely to buy a product if your favourite sports star, musician or actor advertised it? Why or why not?

Many companies have logos that they want us to recognise. Often they put the logo as large as possible on their clothing. When people wear these clothes, they are helping to advertise the product.

Fair deals?

In poorer countries, several companies might compete for a deal with a big company in the United States. Sometimes the company that agrees to do the job for the cheapest price wins the deal. However, this often means that the company will not make much profit. As a result, staff are sometimes encouraged to work long hours for little pay. It also means these companies have less money to spend on buying and maintaining machines that prevent environmental problems.

In the 1980s, some people in the West found out how hard it was for overseas workers. People **boycotted** products from targeted companies. As a result, there is now more pressure on companies to ensure workers are treated fairly. However, there is still a long way to go before conditions are ideal.

boycott to refuse to buy something as a way of making a protest

This woman works in Laos, one of the poorest countries in Southeast Asia. She earns about 33 pence a day making clothes for the United States. This is enough to survive, but not enough to live well.

Campaigns such as 'Buy American' ask people to buy goods made in their own country. Their aim is to help local industries.

Fair trade products

Many poorer people make their living in traditional ways, such as farming. Sometimes it is hard for them to compete with large-scale farms and other producers. Fair trade organisations try to help these people market and sell their products. These organisations aim to give workers a fair price and good working conditions. They also try to ensure that the work itself does not harm the environment. Fair trade products in supermarkets are usually labelled so that shoppers can easily recognise them.

Factories where staff work for long hours in poor conditions and receive little pay are sometimes called 'sweatshops'.

Trade around the world

Protest for the poor

NEW YORK, UNITED STATES – These people attended an anti-sweatshop rally held in New York City. They were protesting against the poor working conditions of many clothing manufacturers around the world.

Best dressed bananas

GLASTONBURY, UNITED KINGDOM – In England, some people dressed up as enormous bananas to help promote fair trade bananas. They attended an annual festival in the town of Glastonbury.

Opened up to trade

HO CHI MINH CITY, VIETNAM – Vietnam used to be a strict communist country. However, in the last 20 years, it has opened up to trade with the West. This woman works in a shoe factory in the country's largest city, Ho Chi Minh City.

Possible law changes

Shanghai, China – The Chinese government has debated some changes to its labour laws that could improve conditions for Chinese workers. However, some international corporations have lodged complaints for fear of increased costs. They want to block the law changes.

Cross border exploits

Pyongyang, North Korea – Poverty is a huge problem in this communist country. Some South Korean manufacturers have opened factories in North Korea. They have hired North Korean staff, who often work for less pay than South Korean or Chinese workers.

Scent of hard work

Nairobi, Kenya – Kenya exports many fresh flowers to Europe. Conditions for the workers are often poor. However, the company where this woman works has a fair trade certificate. It shows that the workers here are treated fairly.

What's your opinion?

Trade between countries allows us to buy a world of different products without leaving our hometown. However, the business of exporting and importing isn't always fair. International organisations, such as the United Nations, try to create rules that make trade fairer. However, many people feel that there is a long way to go before conditions are actually fair.

- Do you think **consumers** have the power to make the world a fairer place? How can the products we buy make a difference?

- If people buy more locally produced products, how will that help people in the United Kingdom? What would be the effect of this change on factories overseas and on their workers?

> **Not everyone in the West is wealthy. My family can't afford expensive things. We buy cheaper, imported stuff because we have to. The factory where my dad worked closed down because the phones that were made there are now made overseas. It is unfair for my dad. It's also unfair for the workers overseas.**

consumer someone who buys and uses products and services

Think tank

Do your own research at the library, on the Internet, or with a parent or teacher to find out more about trading around the world and what some people are doing to improve working conditions.

1 What do you think your clothes say about you?

2 Imagine that you ruled the world. What laws would you create to make things fairer both at home and overseas?

3 How can young people help make the world a fairer place? Think about the choices you make when you buy products such as clothing and electronics.

Glossary

boycott to refuse to buy something as a way of making a protest

consumer someone who buys and uses products and services

import to bring goods into a country from another country